The Good King

Melodi Hawley c/o City on a Hill Press
294 Crossroads Drive
Mount Hope, West Virginia 25880
www.melodihawley.com

Ordering Information:
For details, contact info@melodihawley.com

Hardcover ISBN 978-0-9993412-1-6
Softcover ISBN 978-0-9993412-2-3
Digital ISBN 978-0-9993412-3-0

Printed in the United States of America

First Edition

Acknowledgments

A very special "thank you" is due to the many who attributed time and talent to this work for the purpose of spreading the Gospel of Jesus.

To Lily Bailey, Elyse Boland, Rich Todd, and Travis Cutshaw, my precious friends and team members: thank you for your unique brilliance and creative collaboration in the pre-illustration staging, graphic, and audio works of this book.

To Jennifer Minigh, my friend and co-laborer in the faith: thank you for your wisdom, guidance, and gentle "push." Without you, I would not be a published author.

To Carla Bower, for your honest feedback and selfless desire to help see this work communicated with excellence.

To Kevin Dale Brock: I am forever *grateful* for your hard work, *humbled* by your purity of heart, and *in awe* of your beautiful gift for illustration. Thank you for helping to make the images in my head become a tangible reality!

May this work outlive us all, for the glory of Jesus Christ.

Scan this code to hear the author read the story with
music and sound effects!

the Good King

By Melodi Hawley
Illustrated by Kevin Dale Brock II

In memory of my daddy, Thomas Fant,
who taught me the love of Jesus from my earliest memories.
Daddy, thank you for fathering "little girl me" so well.

Incarnation

"into flesh", when God became one of us, to save us all.

The Word became flesh and blood and moved into the neighborhood.
We saw the Glory with our own eyes.
John 1:14 (MSG)

Once upon a time, there lived a Good King. This King was pure of heart and full of love. His eyes were warm and from his mouth came words of life and truth. The Good King had so much love to share that he decided to build a kingdom for any who wanted family. So, from his own strength and wisdom he built… The Good Kingdom.

The Good Kingdom was a land filled with light and peace. Here, there was no evil or pain and no sadness or fear. The Good King loved his kingdom, and he ruled his people with gentleness and care.

However, just outside the boundaries of
The Good Kingdom lived an evil man,
a dark ruler—The Slum Lord. This wicked
one reigned over the collapsing village called
Slum City.

Slum City was a dreadful place of deep
darkness where people were forced to live in
tents with no heat, no running water, and no
toilets. Trash filled the awful ruins of the city
streets, and evil made its home there.

The Slum Lord was jealous of The Good King. He hated him and wanted to see The Good Kingdom fall. On the edge of where the two cities met, the Slum Lord would send his messengers, worthless troublemakers called The Liars.

From across the boundary line, The Liars would scream truthless things at the citizens of The Good Kingdom. They caused a mighty uproar, scoffing at The Good King and mocking his words. "What does The Good King know? Why should we listen to him? Down with The Good King!"

The Liars worked hard to convince the people that The Good King was not good, that his laws were not written out of love, and that life would be better in Slum City where there were no rules.

Sadly, with trickery and deceit, their evil plan worked.
People drank their words like poison, and many
exchanged the beauty of The Good Kingdom for the
false promises of Slum City.

As the years passed, Slum City's violence grew worse. The farther people moved away from The Good King, the more it caused sorrow. Children were left alone by their parents, and with each new generation, Slum City became darker. Because there were no toilets in Slum City, its people were forced to use something called The Waste Pit, a deep trench built into the ground in the most shameful part of the city.

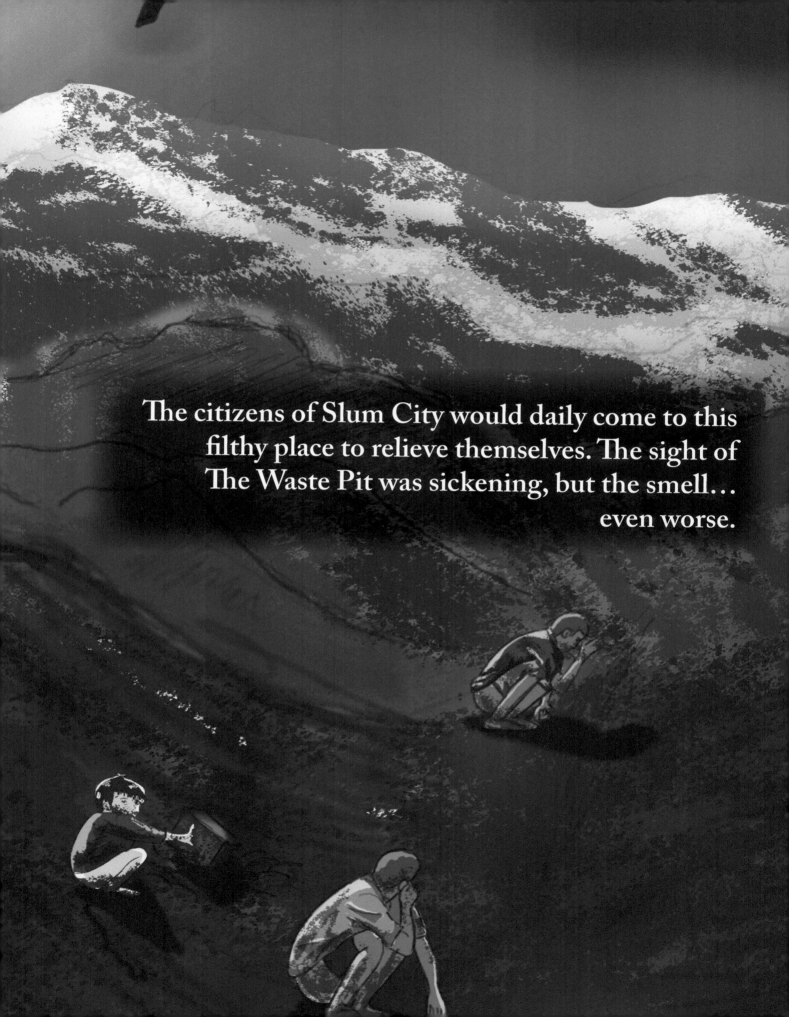

The citizens of Slum City would daily come to this filthy place to relieve themselves. The sight of The Waste Pit was sickening, but the smell…
even worse.

It wasn't long before something tragic began to happen on the edge of that evil city in its most dangerous place. As more and more children without parents filled the streets, the little ones of Slum City began falling *into* The Waste Pit.

Because the pit was so deep and the children were not strong enough to pull themselves out, they became trapped. They suffered. Some even drowned in human waste. The sound of their weeping and crying could be heard from far away. However, the stench was so dreadful, and the sight so shocking—no one was willing to rescue them.

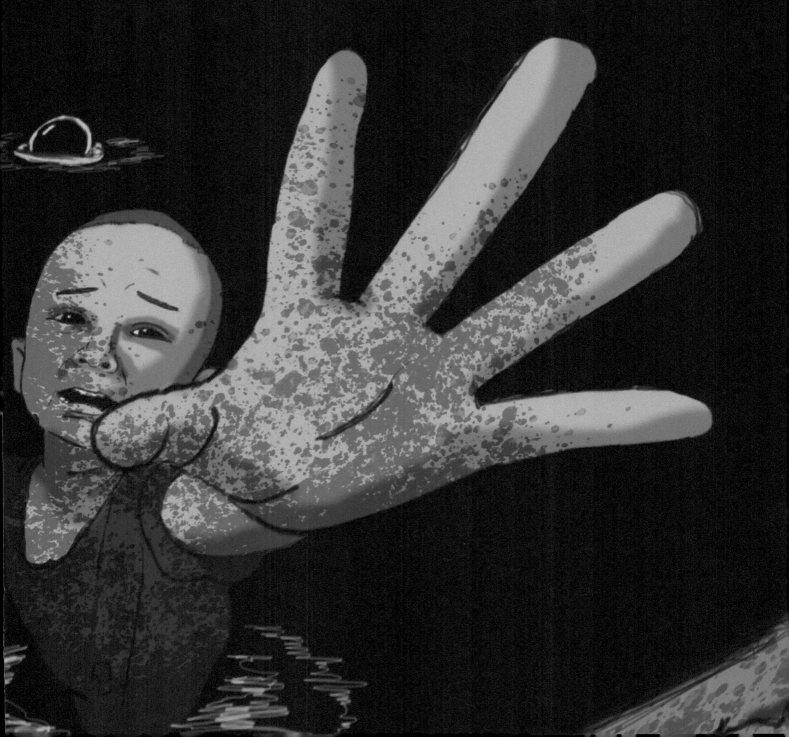

Soon, the cries of the children of Slum City reached The Good King's ears and broke his heart. As he stood facing that awful place, he ached for the suffering, drowning children until he could no longer stand it.

Moved with compassion, the king left his beautiful castle, mounted his royal horse, and rode majestically toward Slum City. But would The Good King *really* cross the boundary line? *Would he dare* leave the beauty of The Good Kingdom to enter the filth of Slum City?

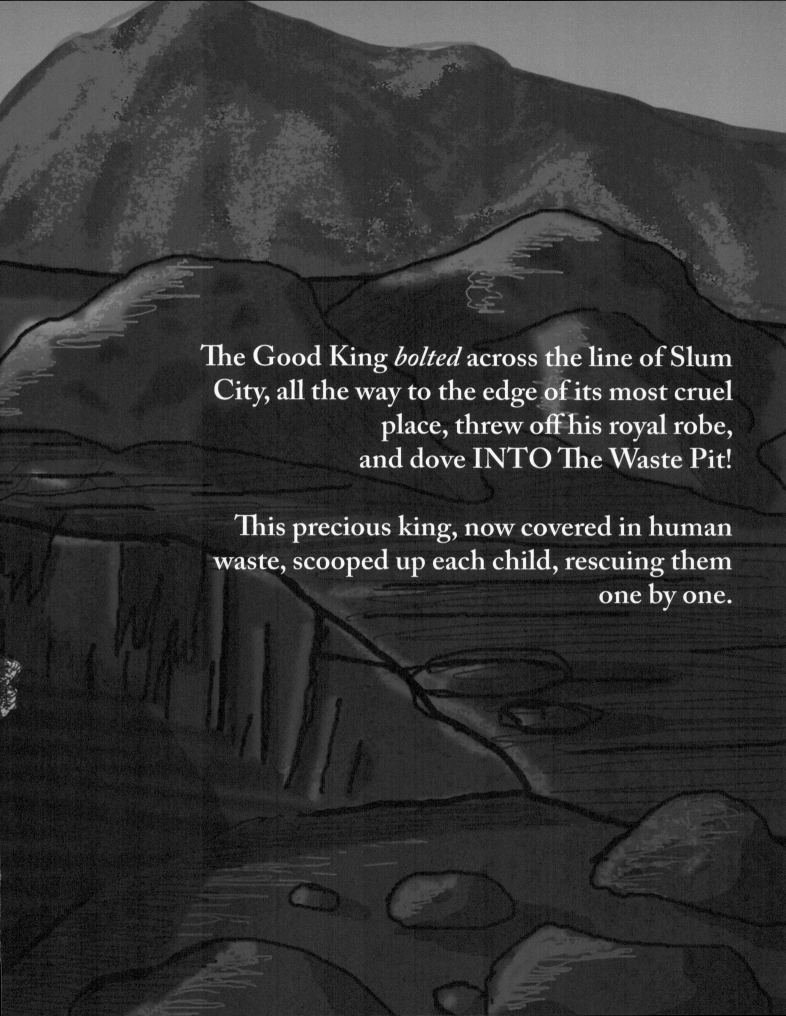

The Good King *bolted* across the line of Slum City, all the way to the edge of its most cruel place, threw off his royal robe, and dove INTO The Waste Pit!

This precious king, now covered in human waste, scooped up each child, rescuing them one by one.

Child after child, he pulled them into the warmth of his safe, loving arms. He wiped the tears that dripped from their eyes and cleaned their stained skin with his own noble robe. He whispered words of comfort into their tiny ears until their crying was calmed. Then, The Good King placed the children on his horse and took them back to The Good Kingdom.

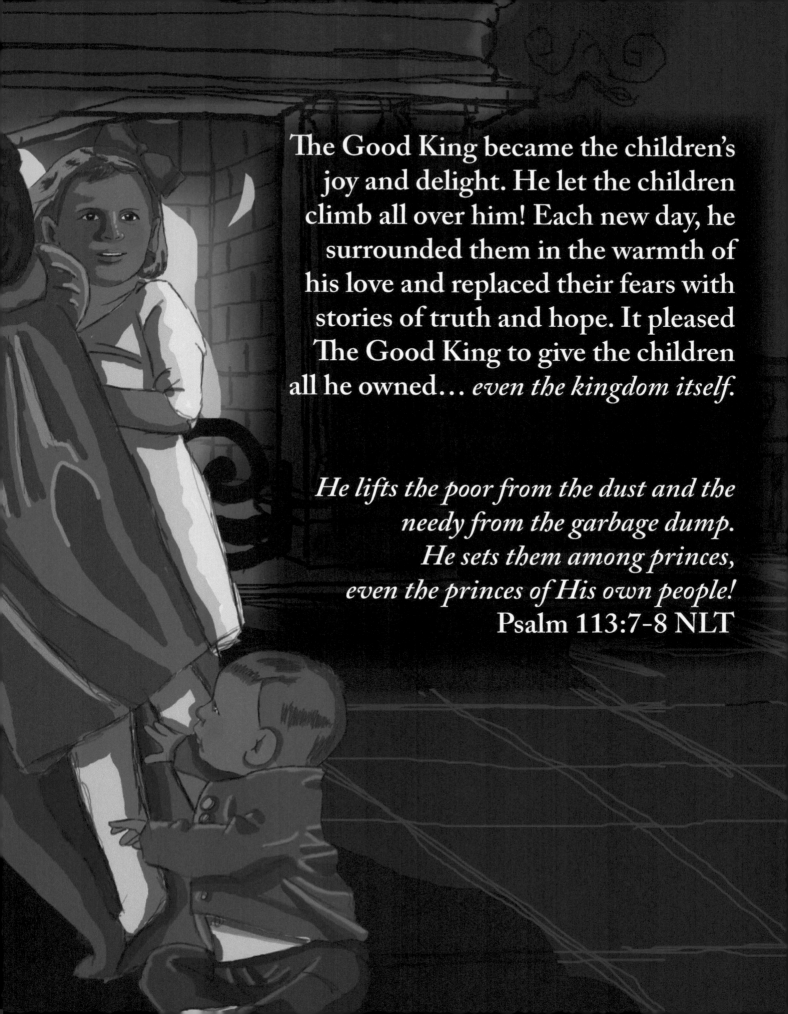

The Good King became the children's joy and delight. He let the children climb all over him! Each new day, he surrounded them in the warmth of his love and replaced their fears with stories of truth and hope. It pleased The Good King to give the children all he owned... *even the kingdom itself.*

He lifts the poor from the dust and the needy from the garbage dump. He sets them among princes, even the princes of His own people!
Psalm 113:7-8 NLT

The End

Let's Talk!
Questions to Ask your Children about "The Good King" Parable

1. Who do you think The Good King represents?

2. Who do you think The Slum Lord represents?

3. Why do you think the people of The Good Kingdom would leave for Slum City?

4. Who are you and I in the story?

5. What do you think The Waste Pit represents?

6. What do you think about the little children going from suffering in The Waste Pit to becoming the King's kids?

7. Do you find it hard to believe that God loves you that much?

Maybe you realize you have never called out to God for rescue from your sins. You can pray right now to receive His love and become His child!

Pray this in faith: *"God, I realize I have made mistakes and I am stuck in them. I am not able to pull myself out. I know I have hurt your heart with the choices I have made, but I also believe that you are ready to rescue me when I call! God, I come to you through Jesus, and I ask that you pull me out of my sins and into your kingdom. Thank you for sending Your Son, Jesus, to rescue me and to die in my place so that I could live with you forever. I give you my life and my future. In Jesus' Name."*

A Note to Parents on the Use of this Book

"Christ is the visible image of the invisible God. He existed before anything was created and is supreme over all creation, for through Him God created everything in the heavenly realms and on earth. He made the things we can see and the things we can't see—such as thrones, kingdoms, rulers, and authorities in the unseen world. Everything was created through Him and for Him. He existed before anything else, and He holds all creation together."
Colossians 1:15-17 (NLT)

It may be obvious that this book is not your average children's story. "The Good King" is a parable—a fictional tale used to illustrate a spiritual lesson. The Gospel tells us that **Jesus never taught without using parables** (Matthew 13:34). They are powerful, effective tools used to bring to life (often difficult) theological concepts.

As a mother of four children, I enjoy reading to my kids. I especially love reading them the type of thought-provoking short stories that leave the reader with more questions than they answer. I see so much value in stimulating my children's creativity, refining their literacy, provoking their curiosity, and encouraging a widened vocabulary.

As a Christian leader, however, I am burdened that an entire generation is growing up unaware of basic tenets of the Christian faith. I fear that biblical concepts once common knowledge to even the youngest of Christians may be lost unless we are diligent to find creative ways to communicate them. *"I will open my mouth in parables; I will utter things hidden from the beginning, that we have heard and known and our fathers have relayed to us. We will not hide them from their children, but will declare to the next generation the praises of the LORD and His might, and the wonders He has performed."* Psalm 78:2-4 (BSB)

"The Good King" was written with the hope of assisting parents in teaching their children about a fundamental Christian doctrine: the incarnation of Jesus Christ (God becoming man).

"For in Christ lives all the fullness of God in a human body." Colossians 2:9 (NLT)

It is difficult for us to comprehend the God of the universe wrapping Himself in human flesh, living and dwelling among us. I do not claim that this book adequately conveys the monumental nature of Bethlehem. But my desire is to, in some small way, remind parents and children of the extravagant love of heaven, which was expressed when Christ became one of us.

In this book, I hope to convey the following truths about the incarnation of Christ:

1. Like the people of The Good Kingdom, we belonged to God, and He desired family when He created us. The Garden of Eden was God's original intention toward us all.

"God decided in advance to adopt us into His own family by bringing us to Himself through Jesus Christ. This is what He wanted to do, and it gave Him great pleasure." Ephesians 1:5 (NLT)

"I thought to Myself, 'I would love to treat you as My own children!' I wanted nothing more than to give you this beautiful land—the finest possession in the world. I looked forward to your calling me 'Father,' and I wanted you never to turn from Me." Jeremiah 3:19 (NLT)

2. Like The Good King, God was motivated out of love. He gave humanity the choice to be in relationship with Him. Love doesn't force or demand reciprocity. (Luke 15:11-31, Matthew 23:37, Revelation 22:17)

"Today I have given you the choice between life and death, between blessings and curses. Now I call on heaven and earth to witness the choice you make. Oh, that you would choose life, so that you and your descendants might live!"
Deuteronomy 30:19 (NLT)

3. Like the people of The Good Kingdom, we were all affected by The Fall. Each of us are embodied both by the helpless children in the pit (victims of The Fall, unable to save ourselves from sin) and also the people of The Good Kingdom (who believed The Liars and left The Good King because of deception). At times, we may even see ourselves in The Liars. We are victimized by sin and yet still culpable for our own choices.

"When Adam sinned, sin entered the world. Adam's sin brought death, so death spread to everyone, for everyone sinned." Romans 5:12 (NLT)
"As the Scriptures say, 'No one is righteous—not even one.'" Romans 3:10 (NLT)
"For all have sinned and fall short of the glory of God." Romans 3:23 (NIV)

4. Like the children in The Waste Pit, we are helpless in our own sin condition. There was no one willing or able to rescue us, except Christ. When The Good King stripped himself of his robe and dove into The Waste Pit, it was a picture of Jesus, the Messiah, emptying Himself of His divine nature to "become sin" on our behalf. *"God made Him who had no sin to be sin for us, so that in Him we might become the righteousness of God."* 2 Corinthians 5:21 (NIV)

"Yet it was our weaknesses He carried; it was our sorrows that weighed Him down. And we thought His troubles were a punishment from God, a punishment for His own sins! But He was pierced for our rebellion, crushed for our sins. He was beaten so we could be whole. He was whipped so we could be healed. All of us, like sheep, have strayed away. We have left God's paths to follow our own. Yet the LORD laid on Him the sins of us all." Isaiah 53:4-6 (NLT)

"For God was in Christ, reconciling the world to Himself, no longer counting people's sins against them. And He gave us this wonderful message of reconciliation. So we are Christ's ambassadors; God is making His appeal through us. We speak for Christ when we plead, 'Come back to God!' For God made Christ, who never sinned, to be the offering for our sin, so that we could be made right with God through Christ." 2 Corinthians 5:19-21 (NLT)

5. As the children in The Waste Pit called out and were heard by The Good King, so salvation comes to us when we realize our helpless state, call out to the One who can save us, and allow Him to pull us out of our filth. When we allow Christ to save us, He takes our filthy garments and allows us to wear His robe of righteousness. **We become children of God, adopted into His family. We become co-heirs with Christ and citizens of Heaven.**

"For God in all His fullness was pleased to live in Christ, and through Him God reconciled everything to Himself. He made peace with everything in heaven and on earth by means of Christ's blood on the cross. This includes you who were once far away from God. You were His enemies, separated from Him by your evil thoughts and actions. Yet now He has reconciled you to Himself through the death of Christ in His physical body. As a result, He has brought you into His own Presence, and you are holy and blameless as you stand before Him without a single fault."
Colossians 1:19-22 (NLT)

"Now if we are children, then we are heirs—heirs of God and co-heirs with Christ." Romans 8:17 (NIV)

6. Like The Good King, Christ was MOVED with compassion. Compassion is different than pity—compassion gets involved. **The concept of incarnation (God becoming man) is so important because it demonstrates how mindful the God of Heaven is to lowly humanity.** Because He became one of us, He feels what we feel and can sympathize with our pain.

"When He saw the crowds, He had compassion on them, because they were harassed and helpless, like sheep without a shepherd." Matthew 9:36 (NIV)

"This High Priest of ours understands our weaknesses, for He faced all of the same testings we do, yet He did not sin." Hebrews 4:15 (NLT)

"But when the right time came, God sent His Son, born of a woman, subject to the law. God sent Him to buy freedom for us who were slaves to the law, so that He could adopt us as His very own children. And because we are His children, God has sent the Spirit of His Son into our hearts, prompting us to call out, 'Abba, Father.' Now you are no longer a slave but God's own child. And since you are His child, God has made you His heir." Galatians 4:4-7 (NLT)

"Do not be afraid, little flock, for your Father has been pleased to give you the kingdom." Luke 12:32 (NIV)

I was tempted to "clean up" this story, exchanging the Waste Pit for a garbage dump. However, in order to fully understand the extent of the sacrifice made on our behalf at Calvary, to fully appreciate the incarnation of Christ, we must realize the true depths Jesus had to plunge in order to secure our rescue. When we minimize our own sin because we are disturbed by it, we risk diluting the magnitude of what was done for us on the cross.

The King James Version translates the verse at the end of this story (Psalm 113:7) more accurately than the New Living Version. It says, *"He raiseth up the poor out of the dust, and lifteth the needy out of the **dunghill**."* What a picture of selfless love is the cross of Christ! Isn't it amazing that the God of all creation stepped down from His throne to live among us? I pray as you read this book your family will experience a renewed awe and deeper understanding of the love of God. My earnest prayer is that adults and children alike will come to saving faith in Christ through this simple children's parable.

May you share beautiful teaching moments with your children each time this story is read, and may we all plunge further into the knowledge of the extravagant love of our Good King.

"May you have the power to understand, as all God's people should, how wide, how long, how high, and how deep His love is." Ephesians 3:18 (NLT)

"We read that Christ became flesh and dwelt among us. It's easy to miss the weight of this statement because we have so 'sanitized' the manger. The hay is clean, the animals are clean, there is a warm glow of cozy light as the shepherds gather around. But it goes beyond the physical filth that Christ endured in His birth. Christ, who was perfect and sinless came to this sinful, broken world full of murder, hatred, envy, wars, jealousy, lying, and every sin imaginable. He descended to us as we wallowed in the sewer of our sin so that he might lift us out and cleanse us of all of it. The 'fall' was just that; it was a collapse into utter filth that we are powerless to escape from. Christ crawled into this sewer to save those He loved."

Thomas Slawson

CPSIA information can be obtained
at www.ICGtesting.com
Printed in the USA
LVHW070147141120
671609LV00015B/582